This is a big truck.

This is a big hammer.

Build Big!

By Ray Trocaro
Illustrated by John Mantha

This is a big backhoe.

This is a big ladder.

5

This is a big bucket.

This is a big house for
a BIG family!

Big Picture Glossary

backhoe

truck

hammer

ladder

bucket